KU-361-005

Penguin  Readers

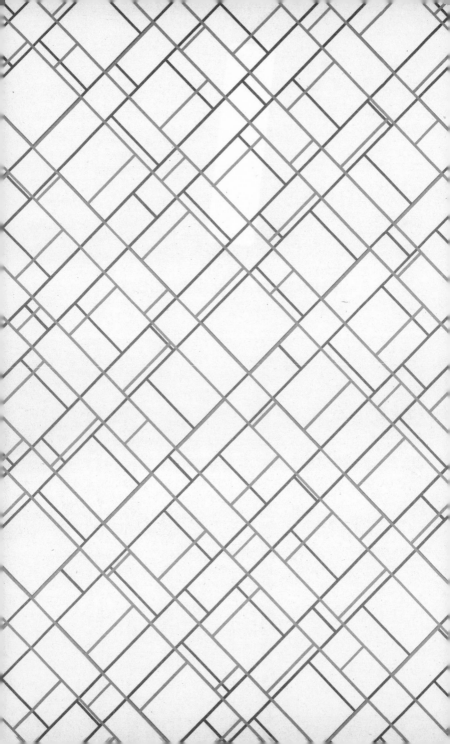

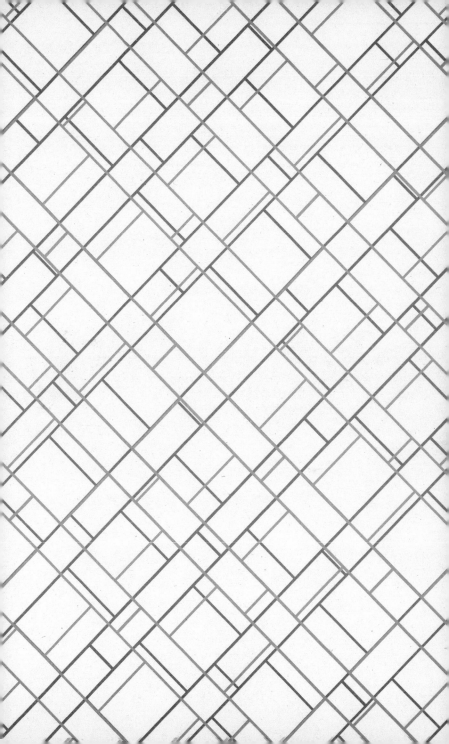

Penguin Readers

THE HOUND OF THE BASKERVILLES

SIR ARTHUR CONAN DOYLE

LEVEL

S

RETOLD BY ANNA TREWIN
ILLUSTRATED BY ALEX OXTON
SERIES EDITOR: SORREL PITTS

PENGUIN BOOKS

UK | USA | Canada | Ireland | Australia
India | New Zealand | South Africa

Penguin Books is part of the Penguin Random House group of companies
whose addresses can be found at global.penguinrandomhouse.com.
www.penguin.co.uk www.puffin.co.uk www.ladybird.co.uk

Penguin Readers edition of *The Hound of the Baskervilles* published by Penguin Books Ltd, 2019

003

Original text written by Sir Arthur Conan Doyle
Text for Penguin Readers edition adapted by Anna Trewin
Text for Penguin Readers edition copyright © Penguin Books Ltd, 2019
Illustrated by Alex Oxton
Illustrations copyright © Penguin Books Ltd, 2019
Cover illustration by Tony Cliff

Printed and bound in Great Britain by Clays Ltd, Elcograf S.p.A.

A CIP catalogue record for this book is available from the British Library

ISBN: 978–0–241–37530–3

All correspondence to
Penguin Books
Penguin Random House Children's Books
80 Strand, London WC2R 0RL

Contents

People in the story

Sherlock Holmes

Doctor Watson

Doctor Mortimer

Sir Charles Baskerville

Sir Henry Baskerville   Mr and Mrs Barrymore

Mr Stapleton and Beryl Stapleton   Laura Lyons

New words

bog

criminal

dead

Devon, England

doctor

frightened

hound

letter

moor

servants

Before-reading questions

1 What do you know about Sherlock Holmes? Who is he, and what does he do? Where does he live? Write your answers in your notebook.

2 Look at this picture of Baskerville Hall. Where is it, do you think? Does a rich person or a poor person live there?

3 Look at the cover of the book. What is the story about, do you think?

4 Look at the "People in the story" on pages 8–9 and answer the questions in your notebook.
   a Who is happy?
   b Who is angry?
   c Who is a young woman?
   d Who is rich?
   e Who is poor?

5 Look at the "New words" on pages 10–11 and write the correct words in your notebook.

   a This is a bad person. ....

   b You are not living. You are ....

   c There is a lot of water in a ....

   d This place is in England. ....

   e You write this with a pen or a pencil. ....

Picture definitions of words in **bold** can be found on pages 10–11.

Sherlock Holmes and Doctor Watson are at home.

A man is coming, Watson. He is a **doctor**.

And he lives in **Devon**.

The hound kills the men in the Baskerville family.

Now, Sir Charles Baskerville is **dead** – and from a dog, I think!

. . . There are no Baskervilles after Sir Henry. He has no family.

Watson, go to Baskerville Hall.

There is Mr Stapleton and his sister, Beryl. They live near.

And there is Sir Charles's friend, Laura Lyons.

That evening, Doctor Watson takes the train to Baskerville Hall with Doctor Mortimer.

Is that the moor?

Yes. And that is Baskerville Hall.

Watson writes to Holmes every day.

<u>MONDAY</u> Now I know Sir Henry. He is a nice man.

But people are frightened. There is a **criminal** on the moor.

The police are looking for him.

<u>TUESDAY</u> Now I know Sir Henry's **servants**, Mr Barrymore and Mrs Barrymore.

I know Mr Stapleton and Beryl, too.

It is night now. There is a man on the moor.
Is it the criminal?

Mr Barrymore is in the garden. Why?

<u>WEDNESDAY</u> Now I understand! The criminal is Mrs Barrymore's brother.

Mr Barrymore is giving him food and clothes – Sir Henry's old clothes . . .

That evening, Watson sees a man on the moor.

Let's speak to Sir Henry.

Holmes and Watson go to Baskerville Hall.

I can help you.

Now, please listen.

That night, Sir Henry has dinner with the Stapletons.

Thank you. I can walk home.

Sir Henry walks home on the moor.

But Mr Stapleton is behind him . . .

Now Mr Stapleton is running.

But Mr Stapleton runs into a **bog** . . .

We cannot help him.
He is dead.

The three men find Beryl Stapleton at home.

Holmes knows Beryl's story.

Mr Stapleton sees Laura Lyons.

Laura writes the note to Sir Charles.

That evening, Sir Charles waits for Laura.

But Stapleton comes – with his dog!

It's the hound!

Then, Sir Charles is dead.

My husband is a bad man.
Sir Charles is dead, and I am sad.

During-reading questions

Write the answers to these questions in your notebook.

1 Where is Sherlock Holmes at the start of the story?

2 Who does Sherlock Holmes live with?

3 Where is Doctor Mortimer from?

4 Who does Doctor Mortimer say is now dead?

5 Who does Doctor Mortimer say is staying at Baskerville Hall?

6 Who lives near Baskerville Hall?

7 What does Doctor Watson write every day?

8 On page 27, who is on the moor?

9 What is Sherlock Holmes doing on the moor?

10 How does Mr Stapleton die?

11 Does Laura Lyons meet Sir Charles at 8 p.m. on the moor?

12 How does Sir Charles die?

After-reading questions

1 Why does Doctor Mortimer visit Holmes and Watson?

2 Doctor Mortimer tells the story of the hound of the Baskervilles. What is the story?

3 "No, I have work, Doctor Mortimer," says Holmes. Why does he say this?

4 Why does Mr Barrymore go into the garden at night?

5 "Mr Stapleton is from the Baskerville family," says Holmes. Why is this important?

6 Why does the criminal die?

7 Why does Mr Stapleton kill Sir Charles?

8 Why does Mr Stapleton call Beryl his "sister"?

9 Why does Laura Lyons write a note to Sir Charles?

10 Is there a "hound of the Baskervilles"?

11 Who is good in the story, do you think? Who is bad?

Exercises

1 **Match the words to the pictures. Write your answers in your notebook.**

Example: 1 − e

1 doctor

2 hound

3 servants

4 bog

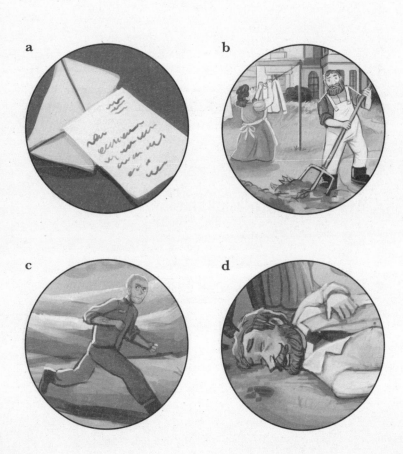

a

b

c

d

5 moor

6 letter

7 dead

8 criminal

e

f

g

h

2 **Write the correct names in your notebook.**

1 .....*Sherlock Holmes*..... lives in London.

2 .... lives with Sherlock Holmes.

3 .... is Sir Charles's brother.

4 .... are servants.

5 .... is Mr Stapleton's wife.

6 A .... lives on the moor. He is
Mrs Barrymore's brother.

7 .... runs into a bog and dies.

8 .... loves Mr Stapleton.

3 **Order the story by writing *1–8* in your notebook.**

a .... Mr Stapleton and his dog meet Sir Charles.

b .... Watson goes to Devon.

c .... Doctor Mortimer speaks to Holmes and Watson.

d ...*1*... Laura Lyons writes to Sir Charles.

e .... Sir Charles dies.

f .... Mr Stapleton dies.

g .... Watson meets Holmes on the moor.

h .... The criminal dies.

4 **Write the correct verbs in your notebook.**

1 Sherlock Holmes and Doctor Watson **is / *are*** at home.

2 Doctor Mortimer **live / lives** in Devon.

3 The hound and the criminal **live / lives** on the moor.

4 Sir Henry Baskerville **live / lives** at Baskerville Hall.

5 "No, I **have / has** work, Doctor Mortimer."

6 Watson **write / writes** to Holmes every day.
7 "Now I **know / knows** Sir Henry's servants."
8 Mr Stapleton **run / runs** into a bog.

5 **Match the two parts of the sentences in your notebook.**
Example: 1 – f

1 Now I know Sir Henry's servants,   **a** dead, too, Beryl.
2 There is Mr Stapleton and   **b** on the moor.
3 There are no Baskervilles   **c** his sister, Beryl.
4 There is a criminal   **d** doing here?
5 Please meet me tonight   **e** after Sir Henry.
6 Holmes! What are you   **f** Mr Barrymore and
                                            Mrs Barrymore.

7 The police are   **g** looking for him.
8 Your husband is   **h** at 8 p.m.

6 **Complete these sentences in your notebook, using the adjectives from the box.**

dead	nice	bad	sad	frightened

1 Sir Charles is ......*dead*......
2 Doctor Mortimer is ....
3 Sir Henry is ....
4 Laura Lyons is ....
5 Mr Stapleton is ....

57

7 **Correct these sentences in your notebook.**

1 Sherlock Holmes lives in Devon.
   *Sherlock Holmes **does not live** in Devon.*

2 "Now, Sir Henry Baskerville is dead."

3 A criminal lives in Baskerville Hall.

4 "I cannot help you."

5 Sir Henry does not walk home on the moor.

6 Beryl is Mr Stapleton's sister.

7 Laura meets Sir Charles at 8 p.m. on the moor.

8 A hound does not kill Sir Charles.

8 **Complete these sentences in your notebook, using *and* or *but*.**

1 "He is a doctor, ...*and*........ he lives in Devon."

2 "There is a hound, ... it lives on the moor near
   Baskerville Hall."

3 "Sir Henry is a nice man, ... people are frightened."

4 "It is night now, ... there is a man on the moor."

5 "It is the criminal, ... he is wearing Sir Henry's clothes!"

6 Sir Henry walks home on the moor, ... Stapleton is
   behind him.

7 "Your husband is a Baskerville, ... he wants Sir Henry's
   money."

9 **Write the correct answers in your notebook.**

Example: *1 – a*

1 The hound . . .
   a lives on the moor
   b lives in Baskerville Hall
   c lives in London.

2 Sir Henry . . .
   a has a sister
   b has no family
   c has three brothers.

3 Mr Barrymore and his wife are . . .
   a doctors
   b servants
   c criminals.

4 Doctor Watson is staying . . .
   a on the moor
   b in Devon
   c at Baskerville Hall.

5 On the moor, Sir Charles meets . . .
   a the criminal
   b Laura
   c Mr Stapleton.

Project work

1 You are Doctor Watson. Write to Holmes about a day at Baskerville Hall.

2 Who is your favourite person in the story? Write about them.

3 Write a new ending to this story.

4 Find out more about Sherlock Holmes. Write questions and ask a friend about him.

An answer key for all questions and exercises can be found at
www.penguinreaders.co.uk

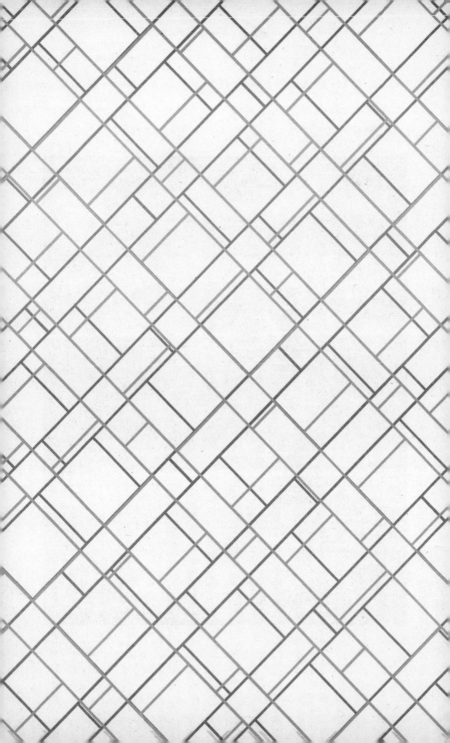

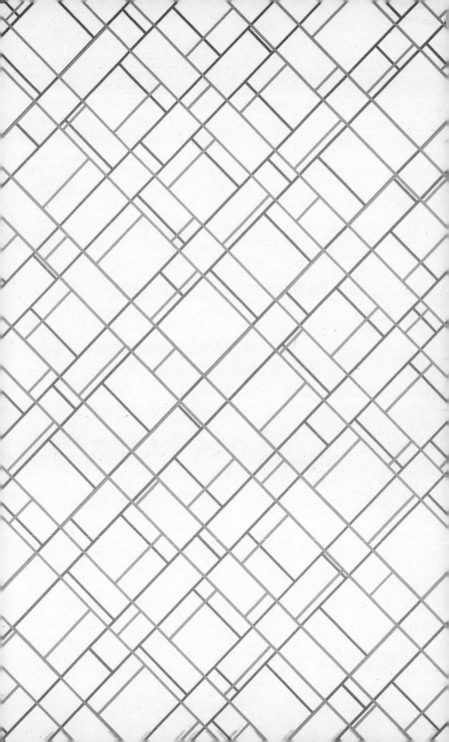

Penguin Readers